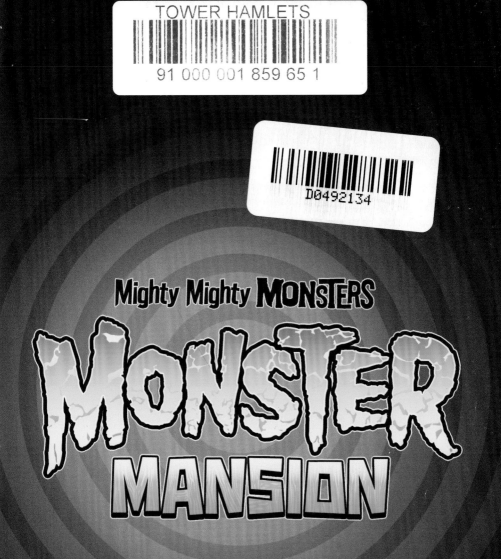

Mighty Mighty **MONSTERS**

MONSTER MANSION

created by Sean O'Reilly
illustrated by Arcana Studio

www.raintreepublishers.co.uk
Visit our website to find out
more information about
Raintree books.

To order:
☎ Phone 0845 6044371
🖹 Fax +44 (0) 1865 312263
✉ Email myorders@raintreepublishers.co.uk

Customers from outside the UK please telephone +44 1865 312262

Raintree is an imprint of Capstone Global Library Limited,
a company incorporated in England and Wales having its registered
office at 7 Pilgrim Street, London, EC4V 6LB
– Registered company number: 6695582

First published by Stone Arch Books in 2010
First published in the United Kingdom in paperback in 2012
The moral rights of the proprietor have been asserted.

Edited by Laura Knowles
Originated by Capstone Global Library Ltd
Printed and bound in China by South China Printing Company

ISBN 978 1 406 23721 4 (paperback)
16 15 14 13 12
10 9 8 7 6 5 4 3 2

British Library Cataloguing in Publication Data
A full catalogue record for this book is available
from the British Library.

In a strange corner of the world known as Transylmania . . .

Legendary monsters were born.

WELCOME TO TRANSYLMANIA

But long before their frightful fame, these classic creatures faced fears of their own.

To take on terrifying teachers and homework horrors,
they formed the most fearsome friendship on Earth . . .

Mighty Mighty MONSTERS

Vlad

Talbot

Witchita

Milton

Poto

Frankie

Igor

Mary

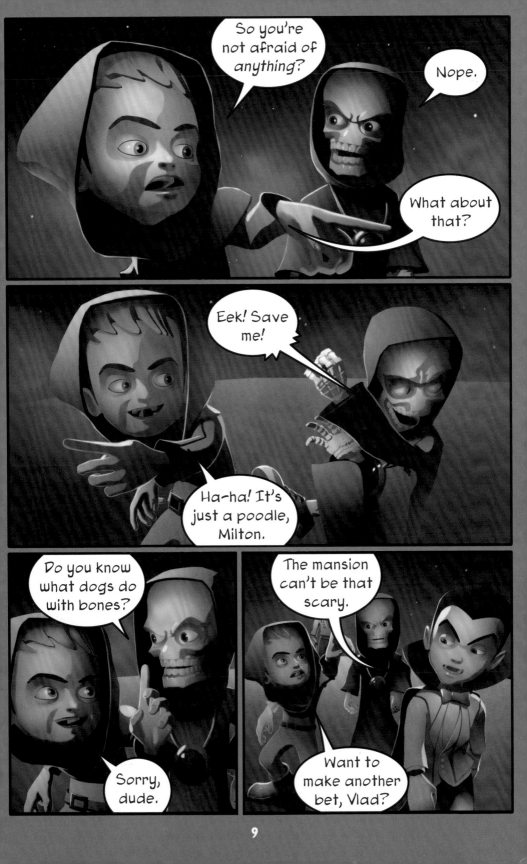

Yipe! I think I'd rather do homework.
Come on, guys. It doesn't look so bad.

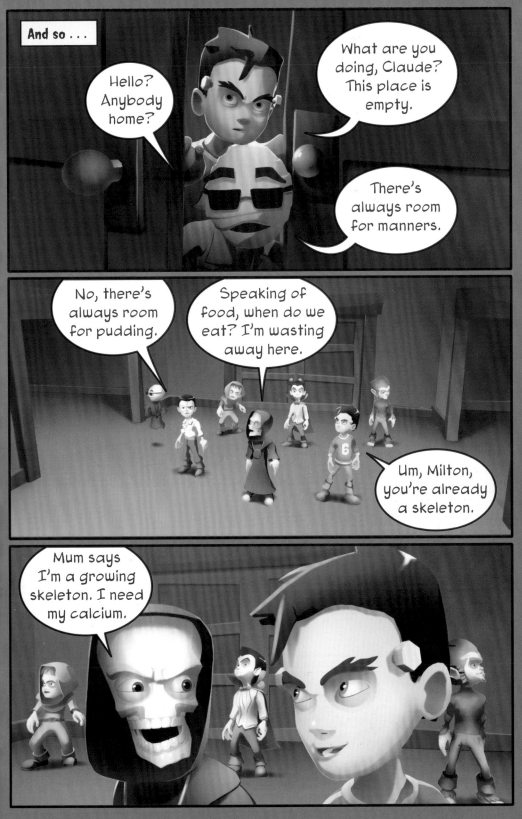

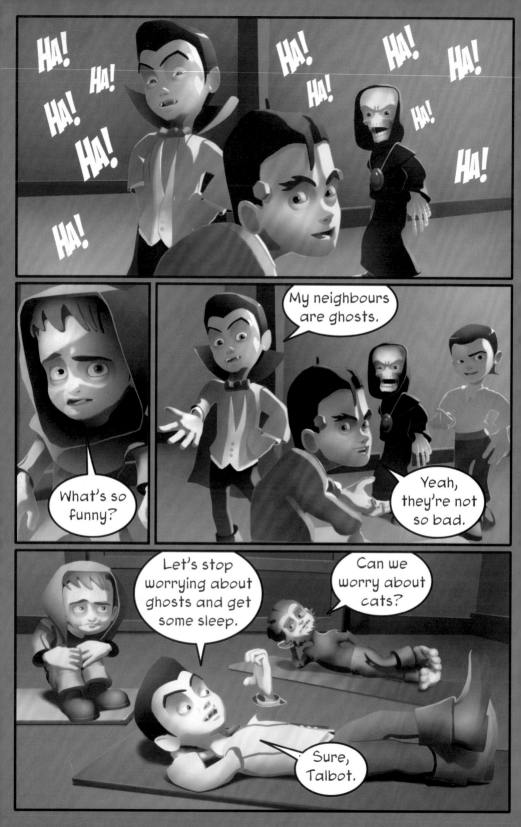

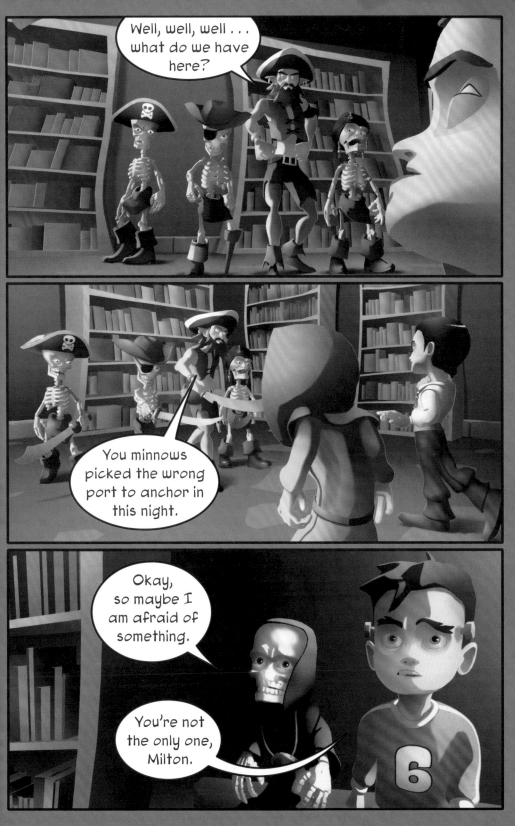

24

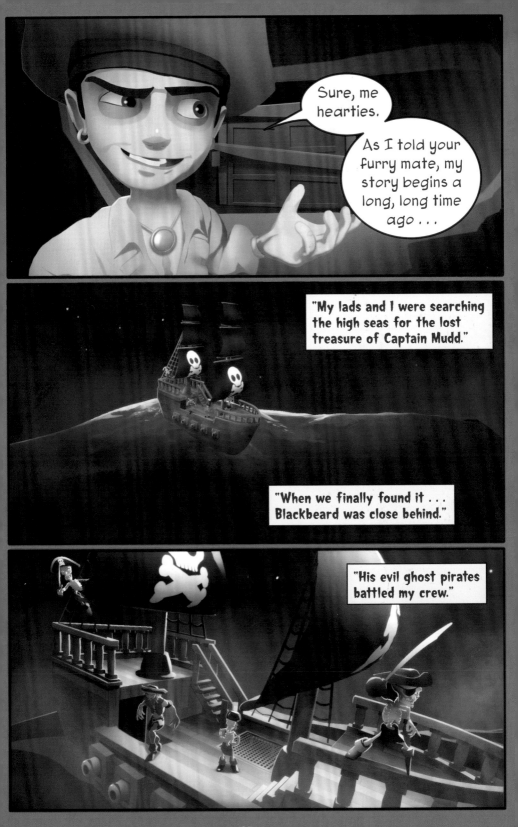

Sure, me hearties.

As I told your furry mate, my story begins a long, long time ago . . .

"My lads and I were searching the high seas for the lost treasure of Captain Mudd."

"When we finally found it . . . Blackbeard was close behind."

"His evil ghost pirates battled my crew."

"During the fight, I headed towards shore to hide the treasure."

"Blackbeard and his men followed, but crashed on the rocky cliffs."

"Meanwhile, I hid the treasure inside the Monster Mansion."

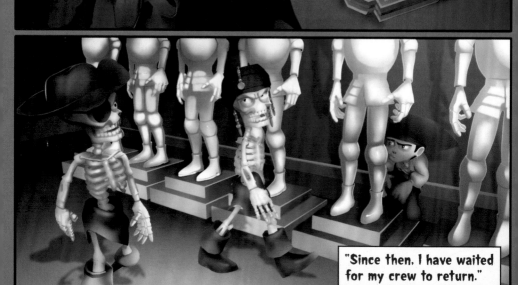

"Since then, I have waited for my crew to return."

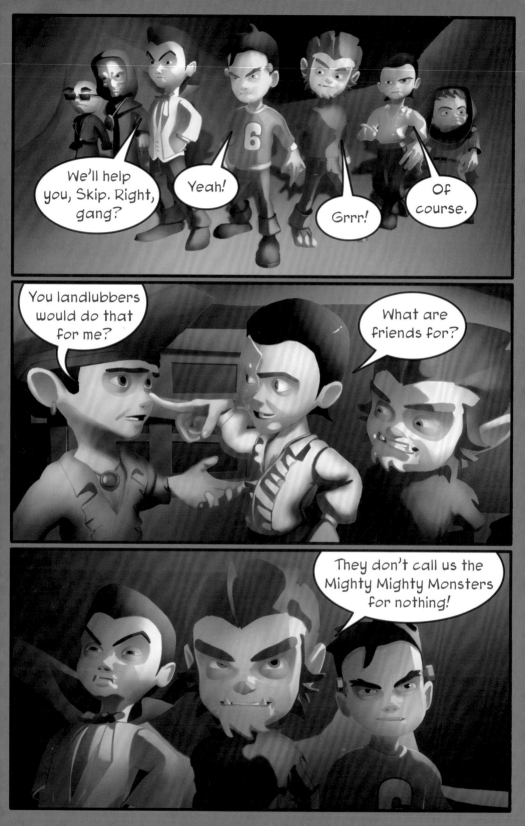

28

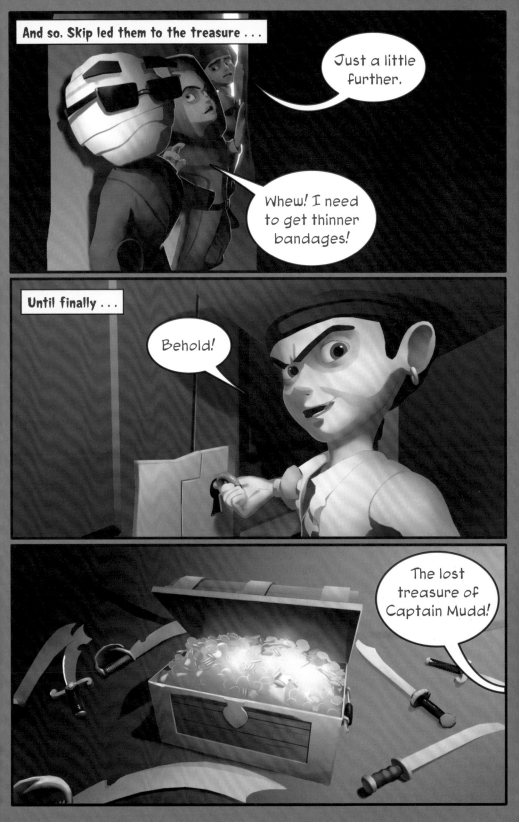

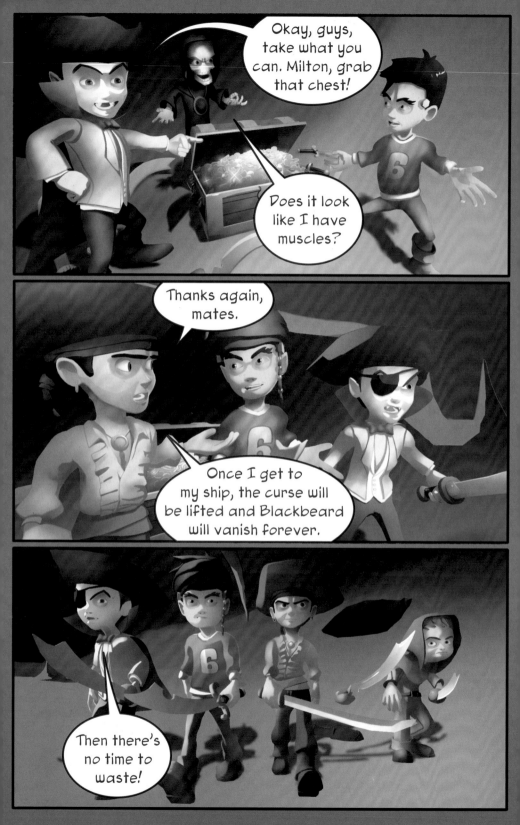

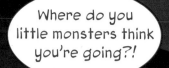

Go back to your pirate phantom zone, you bullies!

I've been scared of you for too long, Blackbeard.
But I've got new friends.
And with friends on your side, you never lose.

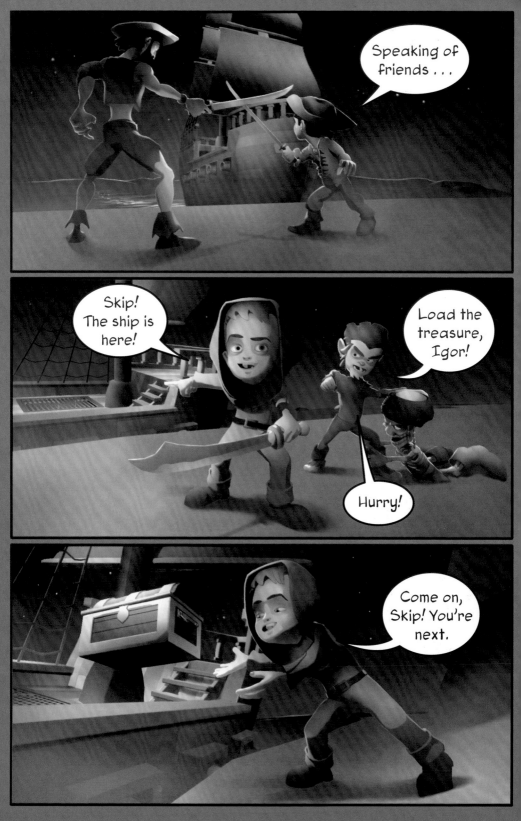

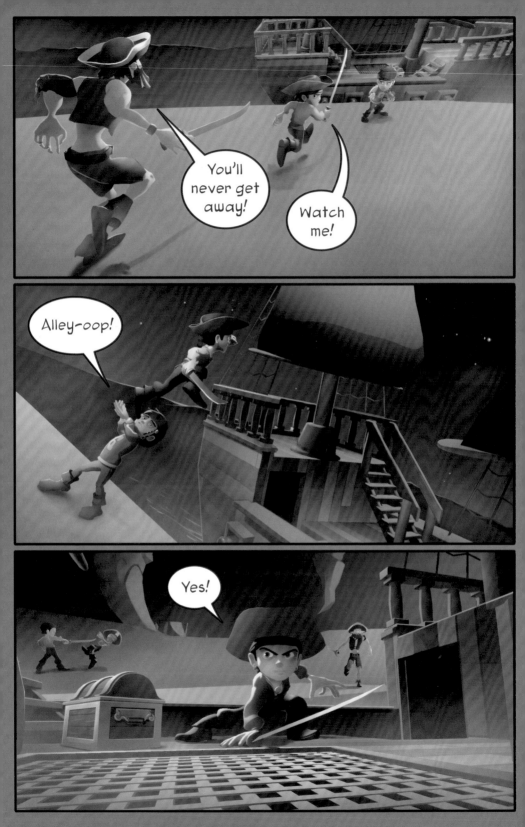

SPOOKY FOREST

MONSTER SCHOOL

FLAME OF HALLOWEEN

CASTLE OF DOOM

Mighty Mighty MONSTERS

...BEFORE THEY WERE STARS!

Igor

Nickname: Hunchie

Hometown: Transylmania

Favourite colour: green

Favourite animal: camels

Mighty mighty powers: super sixth sense; his "hunches" are never wrong; small enough to fit into tiny spaces.

Biography

Orphaned at birth, Igor often struggled to fit in at school . . . until he met the Mighty Mighty Monsters! These fearsome friends quickly adopted him into their creepy crew. And, although he remained shy, the young hunchback brought a special set of skills to the ghoulish gang. His "hunches" were never wrong, and he always steered the Mighty Mighty Monsters the right way. With a clear sense of direction, a keen intuition, and a unique style, it's no wonder he became a monster icon.

WHERE ARE THEY NOW?

Many people believe Igor first appeared in the 1931 film *Frankenstein*. However, that hunchback was actually named "Fritz". The character "Ygor" did not appear until the film *Son of Frankenstein* in 1938.

In the *Son of Frankenstein*, Bela Lugosi played the role of Ygor, Dr Frankenstein's hunchbacked assistant. The actor had already gained fame playing Dracula in the 1931 film.

Other famous hunchback characters include Quasimodo, featured in the 1831 novel *The Hunchback of Notre-Dame*. Disney made the story into a popular animated film in 1996.

ABOUT SEAN O'REILLY
AND ARCANA STUDIO

As a lifelong comics fan, Sean O'Reilly dreamed of becoming a comic book creator. In 2004, he realized that dream by creating Arcana Studio. In one short year, O'Reilly took his studio from a one-person operation in his house to an award-winning comic book publisher with more than 150 graphic novels produced for Harper Collins, Simon & Schuster, Random House, Scholastic, and others.

Within a year, the company won many awards including the Shuster Award for Outstanding Publisher and the Moonbeam Award for top children's graphic novel. O'Reilly also won the Top 40 Under 40 award from the city of Vancouver and authored The Clockwork Girl for Top Graphic Novel at Book Expo America in 2009.

Currently, O'Reilly is one of the most prolific independent comic book writers in Canada. While showing no signs of slowing down in comics, he now also writes screenplays and adapts his creations for the big screen.

GLOSSARY

calcium soft, silver-white chemical element found in teeth and bones

dawn beginning of the day; sunrise

hunch idea that is not backed by proof but comes from a feeling

manners polite behaviour

mansion very large and grand house

mood the way a person is feeling

neighbour someone who lives next door to you or near you

phantom zone area where ghosts live

translate express in a different language

tutor give private lessons to one student at a time

vanish disappear suddenly

Discussion Questions

1. Igor warned the other Mighty Mighty Monsters not to go inside the mansion. Should they have listened to him? Why or why not?

2. Skip was a ghost pirate. Why did the Mighty Mighty Monsters decide to help him?

3. All of the Mighty Mighty Monsters are different. Which character do you like the best? Why?

Writing Prompts

1. The Mighty Mighty Monsters are based on classic movie monsters including Frankenstein, Dracula, and the Wolfman. Write your own story using one of these creepy characters.

2. Write your own Mighty Mighty Monsters adventure. What will the ghoulish gang do next? What villains will they face? You decide.

3. In this story, the Mighty Mighty Monsters helped out a new friend. Describe a time that you helped a friend or family member.

INFORMATION BOOKS

Ghosts and Other Spectres (Dark Side), Anita Ganeri (Wayland, 2010)

Vampires and the Undead (Dark Side), Anita Ganeri (Wayland, 2010)

GRAPHIC NOVELS

Dracula (Graphic Revolve), Bram Stoker, retold by Michael Burgan (Raintree, 2009)

Frankenstein (Graphic Revolve), Mary Shelley, retold by Michael Burgan (Raintree, 2009)

The Phantom of the Opera (Graphic Chillers), Gaston Leroux, retold by Joeming Dunn (Franklin Watts, 2010)

WEBSITE

learnenglishkids.britishcouncil.org/en/make-your-own/make-your-monster

Visit this website to create your own monster. You can also invent your own scary story, dangerous animal, or superhero.

Mighty Mighty MONSTERS
ADVENTURES

The King of Halloween Castle
ISBN: 978 1 406 23719 1

New Monster in School
ISBN: 978 1 406 23723 8

Hide and Shriek
ISBN: 978 1 406 23718 4

My Missing Monster
ISBN: 978 1 406 23722 1

Lost in Spooky Forest
ISBN: 978 1 406 23720 7